Table of Contents

Phonics Reader 46: *Can You Spot the Octopus?*

2   Listen. Read. Write. Vowel **a**

3   Listen. Read. Write. Vowel **o**

4   Listen. Read. Write. Vowels **a** and **o**

5   Spelling Words with Vowels **a** and **o**

6   Let's Review Words with Vowels **a** and **o**

7   Listen. Read. Write. Words to Remember:

    brown, **orange**, **purple**, **white**, **yellow**

8   Reading and Understanding Phonics Reader 46

Phonics Reader 47: *Coyote Helps Out*

9   Listen. Read. Write. Vowels **e** and **i**

10   Listen. Read. Write. Vowels **e** and **u**

11   Spelling Words with Vowels **e**, **i**, and **u**

12   Let's Review Words with Vowels **e**, **i**, and **u**

13   Listen. Read. Write. Words to Remember:

    may, **myself**, **please**, **shall**, **thank**

14   Reading and Understanding Phonics Reader 47

Phonics Reader 48: *Once Upon a Time*

15   Listen. Read. Write. Words with Vowels **a**, **e**, **i**, **o**, **u**

16   Listen. Read. Write. More Words with Vowels **a**, **e**, **i**, **o**, **u**

17   Listen. Read. Write. Still More Words with Vowels **a**, **e**, **i**, **o**, **u**

18   Spelling Words with Vowels **a**, **e**, **i**, **o**, **u**

19   Let's Review Words with Vowels **a**, **e**, **i**, **o**, **u**

20   Listen. Read. Write. Words to Remember:

    brothers, **live**, **own**, **time**, **upon**

21   Reading and Understanding Phonics Reader 48

Assessment Phonics Readers: 46–48

22–23 Test Yourself!

24   Answer Key

    Sticker Page

Workbook

16

Write the word that best finishes each sentence.

Sam takes a _____ .
bath, both, path

Matt's monster _____ is the best!
last, wish, mask

Jan likes to wear her _____ like this.
cot, cap, tip

The _____ work together.
ants, plant, stand

The happy puppy _____ his tail.
wags, legs, walk

Pam put a _____ on the letter.
help, lump, stamp

My name has the sound of **a** as in **cat**.
I am green and I grow on the lawn.
What am I?

Fox wants to go to his den. Draw a line from fox to his den. Connect all the words that have the same **o** sound as in **fox**.

My name has the sound of **o** as in **fox**.
I am a toy that spins.
What am I?

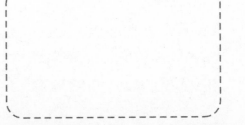

Listen. Read. Write. Vowels a and o

Color the pictures in each column that have the sound of **a** as in **cat** or **o** as in **fox**.

a	o	a	o

My name has the sound of **o** as in **fox**. I am wearing something that has the sound of **a** as in **cat**. What am I?

Find a word below to answer each riddle.
Write the word.

backpack   **dad**   **flag**   **mom**

pod   **socks**

You see me high up on a pole.
What am I?

_____

Peas are inside me.
What am I?

_____

A boy may grow up to be this.
What will he be?

_____

A girl may grow up to be this.
What will she be?

_____

You wear me on your feet.
What am I?

_____

I carry books and ride
on your back.
What am I?

_____

at flies and
it flies!
hat am I?

This is my name
and this is my
favorite snack!
What am I?

Let's Review Words with Vowels a and o

Unscramble the letters to make words with the short **a** and short **o** sounds.

lbcoks _____

agsls _____

nlapt _____

ohsp _____

ndpo _____

I live by the sea.
My name has
a short **a**.
What am I?

I live in a pond.
My name has
a short **o**.
What am I?

Use one of the words below to finish each sentence.

brown   orange   purple   white   yellow

The _____ sun shines.

The trunk is _____ .

He has _____ grapes.

I like to drink _____ juice.

Her tee shirt used to be _____ .

Where can you find
all the colors?

Write a color word to finish each sentence below. Then color the picture.

The grape coral is

_____ .

The black and _____
angelfish has fins like wings.

The clownfish is

_____

with white stripes.

The _____
seahorse does not look like
a fish at all.

Fill in the missing letters to finish the sentences.
Then color the pictures.

The k___ttens l___ck up the sp___lled m___lk.

Fr___sh ___ggs are in the n___st.

A p___g and a h___n sleep ___n a t___nt.

My name has the **i** sound as in **fish**.
I hatch out of something that has
the **e** sound as in **hen**. What am I?

Write the word that best finishes each sentence.

Jenny and Lenny set up a new _____

tent, that, list

The _____ is upside down.

all, cup, pen

Nell's big _____ is on the shelf.

shell, slip, shy

The school _____ picks us up.

bit, lamp, bus

The hen lays _____ in the nest.

eggs, ends, send

The _____ sees a duck in the pon

skip, skunk, grand

I am a young dog that lives with you.
What am I?

Unscramble the letters to make words with
the vowels **e**, **i**, and **u**.

hids

hrsub

elbl

mpup

rckit

dels

I am happy when I'm rolling in this.
What am I? [Hint: vowel **i**]
What am I rolling in?[Hint: vowel **u**]

Let's Review Words with Vowels e, i, and u

Color the pictures in each row that have the same vowel sound.
Then write the words under those pictures. Use the words below.

bed   bus   check   crib   cup
nut   six   tent   wig

Color the pictures that have the sound of **e** as in **hen**.

Color the pictures that have the sound of **i** as in **fish**.

Color the pictures that have the sound of **u** as in **drum**.

This is where you sleep. What am I?

A baby sleeps here. What am I?

Use one of the words below to finish each sentence.

may   **myself**   **Please**   **shall**   **Thank**

I _____ ride my bike.

He _____ pick the duck.

I made a cake all by _____ .

_____ can you help my cat?

_____ you for the gift.

Twins might sleep in this kind of bed. What am I?

Please and _____ you are magic words!

The pictures from the story *Coyote Helps Out* are out of order.
Put them in story order by writing 1, 2, 3, or 4 under each picture.

_____

- - - - - - - - -

_____

_____

- - - - - - - - -

_____

_____

- - - - - - - - -

_____

_____

- - - - - - - - -

_____

Read the words. Draw a line from each word to the thing it names in the picture.

branch   **nest**   **pond**   **fish**   **frog**

man   **trunk**   **eggs**   **stick**   **duck**

sh and frogs
n do this.
n you?

Rabbits and frogs can do this. Can you?

Look at this word puzzle.
Find and circle the word that goes with each picture.
Look across and down.

b	a	t	m	f	i	s	h
d	f	o	x	w	c	p	b
r	s	o	c	k	a	i	e
u	h	e	n	p	t	g	l
m	q	d	u	c	k	m	l

Read the clues and use these words to fill in the puzzle boxes.

add	bus	frog	math	net
rock	ship	sink	truck	web

1. You may see a green pond animal...
2. sitting on this.

3. While riding to school on this...
4. you might pass one of these.

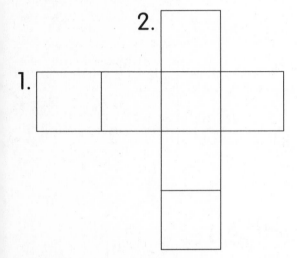

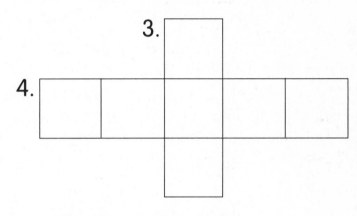

7. A spider makes this...
8. and uses it like one of these.

5. This can float...
6. and it can _____.

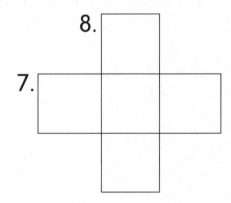

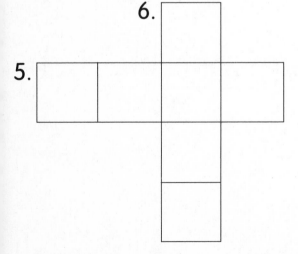

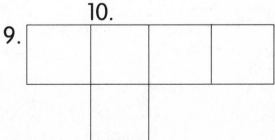

9. The + - = signs are used in _____.
10. When you see +, you _____.

Spelling Words with Vowels a, e, i, o, u

Fill in the missing letters to finish the sentences
Then color the pictures.

The sk __ rt __ s __ n a h __ nger.

The v __ st __ s __ n the b __ d.

The sl __ ppers are __ nder the b __ d.

The s __ cks __ nd __ nderp __ nts are __ n

the dr __ sser.

All the things above
could be packed into me.
What am I?

Finish the story with the words below.

bell   **Cat**   **drum**   **Duck**   **Fox**
Hen   **hops**   **jig**   **Pig**   **quacks**

_____

_____ rings the _____.

_____

_____ plays the _____.

_____   _____

Frog _____ and _____ dances

_____

a _____.

_____   _____

_____ sings and _____.

_____

_____ conducts the band.

Use one of the words below to finish each sentence.

brothers   live   own   time   upon

_____

Sasha and her _____ picked four-leaf clovers

_____

She said, "I wish we could _____ in a castle."

_____

Queen Sasha sits _____ the throne.

_____

Soon it was _____ to go home.

Sasha said, "Dream castles are fun, but our

_____

_____ home is better."

Write a word to finish each sentence below.

Will and Jack like to

_____

_____ stories.

The bears went out because their lunch was too

_____

_____ .

They made up a story about

_____

three_____ .

Will and Jack told

_____

_____ a story.

Underline the word that names each picture.
Then write the word on the line.

1. The clock makes a tick _____ sound.
tip, tock, trap

2. The baby is sleeping on his _____.
back, grow, bend

3. A _____ takes care of pet cats.
ant, bib, vet

4. Some bugs _____ around the flowers.
bed, buzz, fish

5. Rosita _____ the race.
flag, well, wins

Circle the word that best finishes each sentence. Write the word on the line.

1. See the _____ pull the wagon.
   at, in, ox

2. Our bumper cars _____ !
   crash, crib, mesh

3. The hens _____ at the seeds.
   spin, pat, peck

4. Paint _____ on the floor.
   spills, sips, tells

5. The crab digs a hole in the _____ .
   sled, sand, rent

Answer Key

PAGE 2 bath, mask, cap, ants, wags, stamp

PAGE 3 correct path connects: frog, lock, mop, box, doll, rock

PAGE 4 bat, man, log, box, fan, baseball, bat, doorknob, sock

PAGE 5 flag, pod, dad, mom, socks, backpack

PAGE 6 blocks, glass, plant, shop, pond

PAGE 7 yellow, brown, purple, orange, white

PAGE 8 purple, white, orange, brown

PAGE 9 The kittens lick up the spilled milk.
Fresh eggs are in the nest.
A pig and a hen sleep in a tent.

PAGE 10 tent, cup, shell, bus, eggs, skunk

PAGE 11 dish, brush, bell, pump, trick, sled

PAGE 12 check, bed, tent, six, wig, crib, cup, nut, bus

PAGE 13 shall, may, myself, Please, Thank

PAGE 14 3, 4, 2, 1

PAGE 15 branch, nest, pond, fish, frog,

man, trunk, eggs, stick, duck

PAGE 16

PAGE 17 1. frog; 2. rock; 3. bus; 4. truck; 5. ship; 6. sink; 7. web; 8. net; 9. math; 10. add

PAGE 18 The skirt is on a hanger.
The vest is on the bed.
The slippers are under the bed
The socks and underpants are in the dresser.

PAGE 19 Cat, bell, Pig, drum, hops, Hen, jig, Duck, quacks, Fox

PAGE 20 brothers, live, upon, time, own

PAGE 21 tell or make up, hot, pigs, Gran

PAGE 22 1. tock
2. back
3. vet
4. buzz
5. wins

PAGE 23 1. ox
2. crash
3. peck
4. spills
5. sand